TEST YOUR CHI

Handwriting Practice 2

Ruth Fagg

Headway · Hodder & Stoughton

Notes for parents

This book is designed to help your child develop good handwriting habits. Handwriting is an integral part of the English National Curriculum, and good writing is obviously important in all other subject areas.

The book aims to channel your child's natural enjoyment of rhythmic movements through pattern making to the formation of correct letter shapes. A fluent, joined handwriting style will ensue.

Although the pages in this book are addressed to your child, please read the instructions with your child and make sure he or she understands them.

Writers will need:
1   Pencils, coloured crayons and an ink pen.
2   A large exercise book or sheets of paper.
3   Tracing paper. (Greaseproof paper is a suitable alternative.) It is recommended that the patterns and letter shapes are traced because:
    (a) children are encouraged as a good result is given instantly;
    (b) if the same line is traced several times, fluency is established and speed can be increased.

British Library Cataloguing in Publication Data
Fagg, Ruth
    Handwriting Practice. – Book 2. – (Test Your Child Series)
    I. Title II Series
    372.6

    ISBN 0 340 57438 0

First published 1992

Typeset by Litho Link Ltd, Welshpool, Powys, Wales.
Printed in Great Britain for the educational publishing division of
Hodder & Stoughton Ltd, Mill Road, Dunton Green, Sevenoaks, Kent by
CW Print Group, Loughton, Essex.

In this book you will be learning the patterns which form letter shapes and help to make smooth joins. But before you begin to write there are 3 important things to remember.

1 Sit comfortably.

The sketch shows that if you are sitting at an ordinary table you may need a cushion on your chair and a stool for your feet. Jill is resting her feet on a pile of newspapers, firmly tied. Both children have their arms resting lightly on the table ready to hold their pencils well.

2 Hold the pencil correctly and do not press hard.

3 Look at the pictures below and position your paper correctly depending on whether you are left or right-handed.

left-handed

Writing line

Right hand to prevent paper slipping

Centre of body

right-handed

Left hand to prevent paper slipping

Centre of body

Some of the pages have notes about **speed**. This is to help you to get used to writing quickly without spoiling the letter shapes. Quick writing does not have to be untidy.

Patterns

There are 6 patterns, which can grow into letters. It is important that the patterns are well made so that the letters have a good shape. Number 6 is the only one with straight lines. All the others have curves: they should not be too round, but do not let them get spiky either. Trace each short line six times. Then copy each pattern into your own book several times, gradually writing longer rows until you reach the end of the line. Use a different coloured pencil for each row. Changing the pencil helps to relax your fingers. Make sure you hold the pencil *lightly*. Your whole arm should move as you write, not just your hand. Experiment by tracing this line several times as quickly as you can and notice how your elbow moves.

1   This is the under pattern. Sing as you write, 'Swing under, swing under.'

ururururur

2   The over pattern bounces. Say or sing, 'Bounce over, bounce over.'

mmmmm

3   This is the first curly pattern. Say or sing, 'Swing *under* curl back, swing *under* curl back.'

eeeeeeee

4   Here is another curly pattern. Sing or say,' Swing *over* curl back, swing *over* curl back.'

cccccccc

5   A mixture of patterns 4 and 1. Make up your own song to match the rhythm.

acacacaca

6   The zigzag pattern goes down up, down up.

vvvvvvv

On the next 4 pages we shall see how these patterns make the families of letters.

Patterns make **letters**. Here is a family of letters made from the under pattern.
Trace several times before you copy them.

uuuuuu iutl uuuuuu iutljy

All these letters start at the top. *jy* have tails hanging down

t is not as tall as *l*   *itl itl itl jyjy*

These 3 letters are made from the over pattern. There are 3 more in this family
on page 6.

mmmmm nm   Begin with a
very little curve *n m r*
not a spike.

r is made from half an   *n : r*   with a little wave to
separate it from the next   *r r r r r r*
letter.

nmnrnr rim trim liner my

Are you sitting comfortably and holding your pencil *lightly*?
Here are three ways of mixing the two patterns. Copy using colours.

Now for more letters made from the over or bouncing pattern. Trace and copy them.

mmmmm hhhhh mmmmm

All these letters start at the top

h with a kink makes *k* ~ *h* go further round for *b* ~ *b* with a tail instead of a top *p*

h k h k h k h b h b h b p b p b p b

eeeeeeee _____

Because lots of words have *ee* this pattern helps us to begin joining.

keep meet knee bleep peep

1 *eeeeeeeee* Turn the book upside down for the second row. Make several more in different colours.

2 Did you move your whole arm as you made this pattern? See page 4.

ccccc cucucu ccccc

These patterns made the most interesting family of letters.

They all start with c . Trace them and see how they grow.

c cu a c o cu d d cu y g c a c q

Draw another C family on your own paper. Give them names.

Write this sentence in your book. It uses all the letters in the C family.

The cat is too quick for the dog to catch.

S fits into c ssssssccccccc

Trace this row using 2 colours.

S is never a curly snake ℘ , but, always a graceful swan S S S .

ssssss sing a silly song

ssssssccccc

Copy this pattern several times. Use different colours.

CCCCCCCCCC
CCCCCCC

Finish the rows.

C S C S C S   f has a top and a tail   fly flag fluffy

Trace and copy.

fff

Turn the book upside down to make the first row

Row 2.

Finish then trace both rows. Zig zag makes another family of letters.

V W X Z   V V W W X X Z Z V V   Z X W V

van wave box fox lazy dozen

Is your book or paper in the right position? Look at Page 4 again.

CAPITAL LETTERS and numbers

When you are older you will often be asked to write your name and address in
block capitals. This imaginary address uses all the letters of the alphabet. After
you have traced it, pick out the CAPITAL LETTERS and write them in alphabetical
order on a piece of paper. Check your list with the list on the back page of this
book. Then write them at the bottom of this page.

JAMES FOX
67 QUEENS ROAD
WICKLING
YV 4 5BZ
TELEPHONE 018 239

Now copy out the months of the year, beginning with CAPITAL LETTERS.

January February March April

May June July August September

October November December.

Write your alphabet in CAPITAL LETTERS here. Start on the second line.

A

On another sheet of paper practise writing your own address in CAPITALS.

Joins help to make writing quicker, but we must make sure that they are made properly. Joins should not look more important than the letters they join. Letters never change their shape because they are joining. Do not try to join to every letter and only use the pairs of letters as we learn them. On page 6 we saw how easy it is to join two *ee* s. All the letters which end in a little tick can also join to *e* .

a c d h i k l m n t u

Make the stroke longer. This is a **diagonal join**. Trace these.

a c d h k l m n t u

Trace them again fitting an *e* over the join stroke *ae ce de*

Now we can make some words

ce cent de deck he the she me

ie tie ke kept leg nest tell true

Jane will melt the new glue.

Practise some e patterns as on page 6.

CCCCCC CCCC CCCC CCCC CCCC CCCC CCCC

This pattern already uses joins. Trace it several times. Notice how it is used at the bottom of this page.

Other letters can join to ι. Trace and copy the joins and write the sentences in your own book.

ai ci di ei hi ki li mi ni ti ui

Speed tip: do not stop in the middle of a word to dot i or cross t. Do it afterwards.

paid dig their king fruit mist

The Robot likes his kinky tin suit.

The city is quiet at night.

Turn book for row 2.

We can also join to *u* and *y* in the same way.

Speed tip: trace these joins several times.   Get quicker each time. Then copy them.

au cu du eu hu lu mu nu tu

This nurse is on duty. It is her turn.

---

ay cy dy ey hy ky ly my ny ty

Today Amy and Tony made a guy.

The lucky lady rides a donkey.

Are you still moving your whole arm as you write?

CvCvCvCv This pattern helps us to join to all the C letters. We must remember to swing right over to keep the C a good shape (see page 4.) Make a pattern with 2 rows. Turn the book for row 2. Use colours.

Row 1

This time try:

Now you have the rhythm, try some joins. Trace them several times.

ca do ea ho ia lo ma no ta uo

In these sentences underline the joins to a and o. Copy them into your book.

How many cats eat hay each day?

The dog came home to take a nap.

Leo the lonely lion is not coming.

Speed tip: Did you remember to dot i and cross t afterwards?

cacacacacacacacacacacac

Speed tip: Trace this pattern as quickly as you can, still keeping the good shapes.

We can join to *g d q* in the same way.

ca cd ea ed eg eq ca ad ag aq

---

ia id ig la ld nd nq ud ug

Mad Meg hid old bags under big

Ted's bed. Underline the joins to *d* and *g* one in each word.

Now make your own sentences using some of these words: add egg jug round jigsaw bang equal banquet equator sequel.

cacacacacacacacacacacac

Joining after *n m* is quite easy, but we have to be more careful when joining to these letters, otherwise they may change shape.

This is the pattern. Trace it several times and copy it in your book.

mmmmmmmmmmmmmm

Keep this little arch not spiky and not too round.

un in ir u ur in un u

This row is large to show you exactly what to do. Trace it several times.

ururun u u in min mint think

Tina will sing in a minute.

Speed tip: Remember about i and t (see page 11).

unun un un sun funny bunch

Alun Punch had a bun for lunch.

Make up your own pattern using the joins on this page. Look at page 5 and check that you have little curves before n.

in im ˣ Remember to make these little arches before joining not spiky and not too round.

umumimimimimimum

Make up something to say or sing as you trace this pattern several times.

im tim time line mime shining

Speed tip: Finish the whole word before you dot i and cross t.

Tiny Tim thinks it's time to dine.

---

umumum mum sum drummer

The insects hum in the summer.

Copy this pattern into your book, using colours.

Make up other patterns.

eeeeee enenenen emememem

Swing well over to give e   an open eye – make little arches before n m

ei ei en ten en lent en sent went

---

ei en em hem them em element

Remember that r   is related to n . The little arch is very important when you are joining. A spiky join may make r look like v .

ei er sister ai ar car vi ir stir

Penny sent a letter to her brother.

In the dark sky, stars shine afar.

Underline the r in your sentences. Are they well made? r r r r

More joins
Some letters need a different kind of join.

o r v w Join from the top of the letter like children linking arms from the shoulder.
We call these **horizontal joins**.

owowowow Finish each letter carefully before joining.

how now brown cow won wonder

Other joins after o oa oc od og oi om on oo

or os ou ov ow oy Trace several times.

Write these words in your own book, using the joins you have practised.

coal lock hood log lock coin home once for toy

va vi vo vy wa wi wn wo wr wu

Trace the joins. Use them in these words. Write them again quickly.

van vine voice heavy want with dawn won wrong swung

Row 1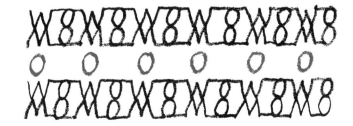

Turn book

You can make lots of exciting patterns from horizontal joins.

Use colours.

Special joins

After *r* we need a little wave before the next letter (see pages 5 and 17.)

ra rc rd rg rm rn ro rp rr ru rv

Trace the joins several times, then use them in these words in your own book
ran arch hard charm torn large crop harp run curve.

Have you made each *r* start with a little arch and end with a wave?

When you write words with double *rr* make sure each *r* has its own wave.

carry merry sorry borrow hurry

We can make a horizontal join from the bar of *f fa fi fo fr fu fy*

Use these joins in words: fan fin fine find for fruit funny jiffy

Speed tip: It is quicker to make a bar after *o* ready for crossing *f* or *t*

$o^1 + f = of$ $o^2 + ff = off$ $so^3 + fl = soft$

$ho^4 + l = hot$ $co^5 + llage = cottage$

Trace these joins. When you get used to it, you will find it is much quicker. To help you to do it automatically make 5 rows of *o* in your book and finish each row with the joins 1, 2, 3, 4 and 5.

Horizontal joins to e also need special care. The neatest way is to make a horizontal stroke and tuck the e under it.
Trace several times to practise.

f fe fever r re here v ve every

w we were ve adventure oe toe

Now very few owls live in towers.

When we have written some letters the pencil is facing away from the next letter, so we do not join after:

b g j s p y. It is also neater not to join after *q x z*.

bigger just quick taxi buzz lost

Do not stop in the middle of a word to dot i and j or cross t, but don't forget to do it afterwards.
Here is another sentence to copy. No joins after y, p, s, x or z.

Last year I paid sixty pesetas at the zoo in Spain.

Some more joins. It is better not to join to the top of tall letters.

Diagonal joins come after a, c, d, e, h, i, k, l, m, n, t and u. *b l h k*

Make a short diagonal stroke. Take your pencil off and make the downstroke of the next letter like these. Trace and copy these several times.

a b   ab   ul   uh   th   c   ck   ll   ll   el   el   all

Has this duck a yellow bill?

There are not many horizontal joins to tall letters, but some we use very frequently so it is important to get them right.

w h   who   what   which   where   why?

Here are a few others. Make up sentences using these words.

kerb   curb   curl   work   lark   mark

owowowowowowowowowowow

On page 19 we learnt about joins after o to f and t. This does not work with other letters so we make the basic shapes first and cross them *afterwards*.

after **after** is a good example and helps you to remember *afterwards*.

Trace and copy these *staff   staff   jiff + y = jiffy*

battle   battle   kettle   kettle   better

Speed tip: Choose one of these words and see how many you can write in one minute.

The crafty kitten hid the little ball.

A page about *S* **and double** *SS*

We can have horizontal joins *os rs vs ws fs*

or diagonal joins but the S does not change its swan shape (see page 7.)

as ds es hs is ks ls ms ns ts us

Trace these joins, then use them in these words. Write them in your own book.

cats sacks hills sums cars rows

cuffs pianos tins tomatoes rust

S is a letter we often use, especially at the end of plural words.

Add *S* to these duck bell star bird stick path bean

Add *es* to these bush patch glass bus fish.

A lot of words have double *SS* . Do not join to the second *S*

pass less miss guess fussy tosses

Trace these words and copy them several times.

Now a tongue twister to use in speed practice. It has all short words so it is easy to remember. Write it several times getting quicker each time.

On ships at sea you can see the

sea as far as the eye can see.

Writing in ink (or pencil)

The rest of this book is written in ink, but you can copy these pages in pencil or ink. Everyone is not ready to change to a pen at the same time.
You can check for yourself.
To write *well* in ink you need to be able to:
1 Sit well.
2 Have the book or paper in the right position for you (see the note below for Left-handers).
3 Join automatically.
4 Hold the pencil lightly. Do this little test. Open the book at your last page of writing. Shut your eyes and touch the writing with your finger tips. If you can feel that your pencil writing has made dents in the paper you are pressing too hard. If you change to a pen you will find it more tiring and the nib will soon be spoilt – so go on practising holding the pencil *lightly*.

Which pen?
Although Ball Pens are popular for every day use, no-one writes really well with them because the little ball at the tip rolls too quickly. The best pen to use for tidy writing is an inexpensive cartridge pen with a firm, straight nib. Held at the proper angle, it makes your writing look attractive. It is much easier to control than you might at first imagine, and you will soon enjoy using it. A substitute for a pen with a metal nib is a fibre tip pen, but these soften with use.

Left-handed people can write with ordinary pens or fibre tips, but there are cartridge pens with special nibs which will help you to write really well and enjoy it! You need to hold the pen well away from the point so that you can see your writing and not smudge what is already written. Keep the book or paper well to the left of your body so that your arm has room to move while your hand writes a whole line.

Everyone needs to relax and enjoy using their new pen. Before you begin copying words, write lots of patterns. This is not a waste of time. It helps you to make the rhythmic movements which will help you to develop your own style but still remain clear. If you sit comfortably and hold the pen well, your writing will not only be legible but also a **pleasure to read**.

Writing in ink

Are you sitting comfortably and holding your pen lightly?

If you have a thick nib you will be able to make thick and thin strokes like this:

If you have a thinner nib your pattern will look like this:

A left-handed nib is shaped so that you can hold it in the same way as your pencil.

If you are right-handed, point your pen like this:

Diagonal joins after *a c d e h i k l m n t u*

Trace to get the rhythm. In your own book, join each letter to a, e, i, o and u.

uuuuuuuuu Join to *i u y* with pointed tops.

vvvvv *mmmm* *nenene* *mememe*

Make arches for n and m and keep open eyes for e.

Trace the patterns several times before you copy the sentences.

We shall buy him a nice tin of mints.

I can swim seventy nine lengths.

nenenenenene Turn book

Make up more patterns like these.

Joins to *r* . Remember the little arch before each *rrrrrr* .

ar ar er er ir ir ur ur tr tr 5 joins.

Trace this sentence which uses all these joins. Copy it and underline the joins.

Mary tried to turn her fire alarm on.

When you write words with *rr* make sure each has a wave *rr* .

Harry will marry Carrie tomorrow.

Here are more words to practise:

merry terrify hurry ferry porridge terrace hurricane.

cccccccccc cs cs cs cs cs

s is still a graceful swan. It does not change its shape.

Joins to *as es is os us* . No join after *s* .

Toss six tasty sausages in spicy sauce.

Row 1

Are you sitting comfortably and holding your pen correctly?

cccccccc   caodgq   cacacaca

Join to these letters making a well-shaped c first: ꞓ ꞓc ꞓa ꞓc ꞓo

ꞓ ꞓc ꞓd ꞓg ꞓq   Trace these joins several times before tracing and copying the sentences below.

Samantha ran fast in a potato race.

Does your dad like egg with haddock?

Remember to lift your pen before tall letters.

al al ll all call el el tell lk lk like

Mr Black sells tall silk hats.

The downstrokes for tall letters should be parallel and even.

ullullullull   Make some other patterns by turning the book upside down as you have done before.

Horizontal joins after *forvw* . Hold your pen well, then the joins will not be too thick. www v̆ v̆ v̆ w̆ w̆ w̆

v̆v̆v̆v̆v̆ ov ou oa oi oy oc or on

os ow or wa wr ra ro ri ru va vo

Trace these joins several times before you trace and copy the sentences.

The moon shone over the frosty town.

Tuck e under horizontal joins (see page 20).

Eleven elves lived in seven caverns.

Here are some words to copy into your book. Check the horizontal joins with the list at the top of this page.

cocoa coin toy clock storm stone roar roses roast arch voice want corn come wrong for fun.

Make patterns from these joins *vavava wowow ouououou*

Here is a word puzzle. The letters **ough** make 5 different sounds. In your book write these words neatly across the page.

cough dough bough ought rough

Find other words which rhyme with them and write the new words in the correct columns. They will not all be spelt **ough**. Check with a dictionary.

A writing tool means anything we use for making the marks we call writing. We can start with chalk or thick crayons and go on to use plain or coloured pencils or felt-tip pens. The last few pages of this book have been written with a cartridge pen. The square-cut metal nib makes thick and thin strokes without pressure. If you have a different kind of nib you can still write neatly. If possible, left handers should use the specially shaped nibs. The tip is curved towards the left so that they do not need to alter the position of their hand. They are made in different widths. Copy these sentences. If you enjoy drawing you could make some pictures to go with them.

No joins after   *b g j p q s x y z*   Keep the right space before the next letter.

Biggles blows the biggest bubbles.

Peggy always giggles in goggles.

The puppy yaps as the jester jumps.

The Queen's quails quarrel about quills.

There are no joins after capital letters.

Vivien Wise uses the Xerox machine in the office.

Mr Robert King lives in Canning Town.

If you look after your writing tools they will last longer and help you to enjoy writing. Pencils should not be allowed to get blunt. Always put the cap on your pen before you put it away. If you have a desk at home keep pens standing upright. Special containers are not necessary. A round tin covered with paper will cost you nothing to make and will protect your pens from damage.

Speed and legibility

We all need to write quickly sometimes. We can prepare for this by making special efforts. Writing is a movement of muscles in arm and hand. Sports and games are also movements of muscles. Before you enter a race you practise running faster each day. We can use the same ideas in handwriting. 5 or 10 minutes daily will get much better results than an hour once a week. Here are suggestions for 5 days.

1   Take some scrap paper (even newspaper will do) and coloured felt pens. Make lots of lines moving your hand and arm across the paper as quickly as you can.

You will probably find that as you get quicker the lines get straighter. If you are left-handed, remember to keep your page to the left, giving your arm room to move.

2   Take some tracing paper and go back to page 4. Trace the patterns several times each – quickly, but keeping good shapes.

3   Copy one join from pages 15, 16 or 17 and build up words like this.

un sun sunny, im tim time, en ten tent en

These are a few examples. You can make up many more.

4   Choose a phrase or a short sentence. Write slowly the first time, gradually getting quicker. Writing races can be fun with friends, but if you are alone use a digital watch, or a clock with a seconds hand. Make a note of your scores.

The clown sat down. The clock at the dock.

The hares have to move more quickly.

How many marry at Gretna Green?

These sentences all contain letters which can be confused. Check yours.

5   Go back to one of the other pages. Copy it into your book. Make a note of the date and the time it took you to write it. A week later try again. Keep setting yourself new targets. You will be surprised at how much you can improve. Remember to sit comfortably and hold your pen or pencil *lightly*.

Quick writing does not have to be untidy.

Pages 11, 12, 14, 19 and 21 all have suggestions about **speed**. Plan another 5 days' practice using these ideas.

Fun with words

The Fly and the Flea.

A fly and a flea in a flue
Were imprisoned, so what could they do?
Said the fly, "Let us flee!"
"Let us fly!" said the flea,
So they flew through a flaw in the flue.

Notice the punctuation and speech marks (inverted commas).
A way of learning where to put them is to draw a cartoon.
Only what comes out of the mouth goes into the balloon!

At the D.I.Y. Sydney Seeley sells ceiling sealer.

Wendy Wate's overweight luggage kept us waiting.

Remember when they plague you,
With words like vague and ague,
That the letters don't betoken,
How the words ought to be spoken.

Spacing and arrangement

Writing looks more attractive if it is well-spaced. Letters which are correctly joined are automatically even, but you need to take care where there is no join.

1   Turn to a new page in your writing book. Write a heading *Space between letters* and underline it. Copy page 28 again. On the next page write another heading *Space between words*, and copy this:

2   The space between words should be large enough for one letter (as in typing).

Minnie orinses oandos aves oaluminium otins.

Write more sentences, putting coloured letters in the spaces.

3   In all your stories and project work keep a space all round your writing. Start new paragraphs about 2 centimetres from the margin.

4   If you need to make lists keep the columns level.

5   Find a page in a reading book where several people are speaking and copy their conversation using "   ", ! ?.

6   When you write your own verses or copy other people's poems enjoy arranging them in different ways.

7   I am sure your relatives and friends, especially grandparents, would be pleased to receive a letter from you. Arrange your letter well, with the address, date and greeting (e.g. Dear Grandma) in the proper places. I'll let you into a secret. You can make a short letter look much longer if you do not start too near the top of the page and leave a margin space at the beginning and end of each line. Arrange the ending on 3 lines in the middle of the page. With love, from, your name.

Patterns

There are a number of interesting patterns in this book. Look back at some you have enjoyed and practise them in a variety of colours. Use them as decoration or borders for special pieces of writing. It is possible to make more patterns, but there is not room for them in this book. Experiment with some of your own.

More ideas

You have learnt a basic style of handwriting which is quick and legible, suitable for everyday use. If you would like to develop a more elaborate style for special occasions, perhaps making your own Christmas or Birthday cards, ask at a library about books on calligraphy.

Size

Writing in a copy book has to be fairly large to show details of the letter shapes and joins. Eventually you will choose your own size. The most important thing is to keep the right proportion for short letters, tops and tails.

Short letters: *a c e i m n o r s u v w x z*

Letters with tops: *b d h k l   t*

Letters with tails: *g j p q ~ f*

has top and tail so it is the size of 3 short letters. *g a f*

Slope

We read from left to right, so backslope writing faces against the way our eyes are moving. Uneven writing is also difficult to read so keep all the downstrokes parallel and even.

Fill twelve dozen big copper jugs with sixty quarts of milk. Practise this sentence. It uses all the letters of the alphabet.

a A b B c C d D e E f F g G h H i l j J k K l L
m M n N o O p P q Q r R s S t T u U v V
w W x X y Y z Z. 1 2 3 4 5 6 7 8 9 0.

A tongue twister – very appropriate for a book on writing.

Write, we know, if written right,
Should not be written wright or right,
Nor should it be written rite, but write,
For only then is it written right.

The last page of this book – but not the end! Go on enjoying writing.